CW00656718

Intermitter

Easy And Healthy Guide To Intermittent Fasting For

Weight Loss, Burn Fat, Slow Aging, Detox Your

Body And Support Your Hormones

(Intermittent Fasting Recipes For Beginners)

Delbert Burgess

Table OF CONTENTS

Egg Salad

Ingredients :

4 boiled eggs
2 avocado (approx. 250 g)
65 ml of water
3-4 teaspoons of curry powder
salt
pepper
Fresh Lemon juice of one fresh Lemon

Preparation:
1. First puree the avocado with the fresh Lemon juice, the water and the spices. This should make a sauce.
2. Then cut the eggs into cubes and mix with the avocado sauce.
3. You can use mayonnaise instead of avocado.

Minced Meat Casserole With Zucchini

Ingredients :

2 tbsp coconut oil

650g minced meat mixed

650 g zucchini

10 0g cream (4 0%)

270g canned tomatoes

65g Emmentaler

salt

pepper

Garlic to taste

Italian herbs

Preparation:

First fry the minced meat with coconut oil and add the canned tomatoes, cream and spices.

 Then cut the zucchini into slices.

Then layer the minced meat and zucchini alternately on top of each other.

Sprinkle the cheese on top and bake the casserole at 300 degrees for 40 minutes.

Goat Cheese Wrapped In Bacon

Ingredients :

2 tbsp olive oil

2 teaspoon mustard

2 tbsp white balsamic vinegar

salt

pepper

2 teaspoon coconut oil

85 g lamb's lettuce

40g rocket

85 g goat cheese

65g bacon strips

Preparation:

1. In the first step, wash the lettuce and arugula and place them on a plate.
2. For the dressing, mix mustard, vinegar, oil, salt and pepper together.
3. Now cut the goat cheese into slices. Then wrap the bacon around the goat cheese slices.
4. Put this in a pan and fry it with coconut oil.
5. Finally, grind pepper over the salad and you're done. Enojy your meal!

Broccoli Cream Soup

Ingredients :

65g cream (4 0%)

4 00 ml vegetable broth

2 tbsp coconut oil

230 g broccoli

Preparation:

1. Cut the broccoli into small pieces and sauté them with oil.
2. Then add the vegetable stock and cook the broccoli until soft.
3. In the next step, add the cream and puree the soup.
4. Finally, season the soup with salt & pepper as required.

Kale Pesto

Ingredients :

2 65 ml of olive oil

2 pieces of garlic cloves

2 pinch (s) of salt and pepper to taste

85 g almonds

230 g kale

25 g parsley

Preparation:

1. First pluck the kale from the stem and wash it.
2. Then peel the garlic and chop it up.
3. Now put all the ingredients in a blender and mix it to a hearty consistency.
4. Finally, you can season the whole thing with salt and pepper as you like.

Chicken Zucchini Alfredo

Ingredients :

4 zucchini

2 tbsp olive oil, virgin

approx. 650 g chicken breast

Sea salt and pepper

2 teaspoon Italian herbs

2 cloves of garlic, pressed

2 25 ml whole milk

230 g cream cheese (double cream)

65 g cup of parmesan cheese, grated

1/2 cup parsley, freshly chopped

Preparation:

First cut the zucchini into a spaghetti shape
with a peeler and place it on kitchen paper.

  Then heat oil in the pan and season the
meat with salt, pepper and herbs.

In the next step, add the whole thing to the pan and fry for 8 minutes.

After 8 minutes, take the meat out of the pan and cut it into thin strips.

Now heat the oil in the pan a second time and add the garlic. Cook until the aroma spreads.

Now add the milk, cream cheese and the parmesan. Season the whole thing again with a little salt and pepper and cook it for 10 minutes.

Finally, garnish the dish with some chopped parsley. Good Appetite!

Spicy Shrimp Kebaps

Ingredients :

2 teaspoon fresh onion powder

2 teaspoon oregano, dried

2 lemons, sliced

6 00 g shrimp

2 tbsp olive oil, virgin

Sea salt and cayenne pepper

2 teaspoon paprika powder

2 teaspoon garlic powder

Preparation:

1. First, preheat the oven to 300 degrees and put salt, cayenne pepper, paprika powder, garlic powder, fresh onion powder and oregano in a bowl and mix them together.
2. Now put the shrimp with the oil, as well as the mixture made in the first step, in a bowl. Then cover the shrimp with it.
3. Finally, skewer them with fresh Lemon slices on wooden skewers and place in the oven for 2 10 minutes. Turn it every now and then.

Coconut Curry

Ingredients :

1 teaspoon salt

2 teaspoon fresh Lemon peel

465g frozen spinach leaves

4 85 g coconut milk

3-4 tsp yellow curry paste (or 3-4 tsp curry powder)

Preparation:

1. Prepare the spinach according to the instructions on the packet and let a pan get hot at the same time.

2. Then add 2 teaspoons of curry paste and a few tablespoons of coconut milk to the pan and stir until it becomes a sauce.

3. Please let the whole thing cook for a few minutes. Then add the spinach and the rest of the coconut milk.

4. Mix everything together and let it boil so that the sauce can thicken.

5. In the last step, garnish the dish with almonds or cashew nuts.

Chicken Chili

Ingredients :

2 tbsp chilli powder

2 jalapeno, cut into small slices

1 tbsp cumin

1 tbsp garlic powder

220g cream cheese (double cream level)

Salt and pepper to taste

2 fresh pieces of chicken breast

2 tbsp butter or ghee

1 fresh onion , finely chopped

2 cups of chicken broth

2 can of tomatoes, diced

90 g tomato paste

Preparation:

1. Place the chicken breast in the broth or optionally in water.
2. Then please cover the meat with the liquid.
3. Now cook the meat for 2 2 minutes until it is no longer pink and then pour off the liquid.
4. Then chop the chicken breast and melt the butter or ghee in a saucepan.
5. Now add the fresh onion s and steam them until they are translucent.
6. Then put the meat, the chicken stock, the diced tomatoes, tomato paste, chilli powder, caraway seeds, garlic powder and jalapeno slices in this pot and stir everything together.
7. Now cook all the ingredients and then reduce the temperature.
8. Then put a lid on the pot and let it cook for 25 minutes.
9. Then add the cream cheese.

10.Now increase the heat and stir everything together in the last step.

Cheesburger

Ingredients :

2 teaspoon salt

1 teaspoon pepper

2 teaspoon of cajun powder

2 tbsp butter or ghee

Cloud bread

245g ground beef

2 slices of bacon

45g mozzarella

65g cheddar, sliced

Ingredients for the cloud bread:

2 eggs (M)

4 tbsp cream cheese

1/2 tsp baking powder

Preparation:

To make the cloud bread, beat the egg whites until stiff and mix the cream cheese with the baking powder.

Lift it under the ice snow and mix it together.

Depending on your taste, you can either make a sweet or a salty version of the bread.

Accordingly, you can either season it with salt and pepper, or sweeten it with stevia liquid. The sweet variant goes in the direction of French brioche.

Then form equal portions and bake the rolls for 45 minutes at 2 65 degrees. Then place the paper over it so that the buns don't get too dark on top.

Now mix the minced meat with all the spices and form patties out of the meat.

The meat is then filled with mozzarella and 2 tablespoon of butter or ghee is heated and the patties are placed in it.

Then fry the meat for 4 minutes and cover with the cheese.

In the last step, fry the whole thing for another 4 minutes and then pour the fried bacon over it.

Broccoli-Cheddar Soup

Ingredients :

2 cup broccoli, sliced

2 tbsp cream cheese

1/2 cup fresh whipped cream

2 cup of cheddar cheese, finely sliced

2 slices of bacon

1 teaspoon xanthan gum

2 tbsp butter

1/9 cup fresh onion

1 teaspoon garlic, pressed

2 cups of chicken broth

Pinch of salt and pepper

Preparation:

1. First, heat a saucepan and fry the fresh onion s and pressed garlic with butter.

2. Then add the broccoli and chicken broth and cook the broccoli until soft. Season everything with salt and pepper.

3. Microwave the cheddar cheese for 45 minutes, until it becomes sticky.
4. Then add the whipped cream and cream cheese to the soup.
5. Add the cheese when you take the pan off the stove.
6. Finally, you can thicken the soup with xanthan gum.

Lasagna In A Pumpkin

Ingredients :
2 cup of mozzarella cheese
1/2 cup parmesan cheese
parsley
Pinch of salt and pepper
230 g sausages
2 yellow Hokaido pumpkin

2 cup of pasta sauce

1/2 cup ricotta cheese

Preparation:

1. First cut the pumpkin in half and core it.

2. Now place one half with the open side down on the baking sheet and pour 4 cm of water over it.

3. Then bake this half for 40 minutes at 2 65 degrees (the pumpkin is ready when it's soft).

4. Now grill the sausages, put them in a saucepan and stir them with pasta sauce and spices.

5. Let the whole thing cook for 2 6 minutes and then mix with the cheeses.

6. Finally, fill the pumpkin with the mixture, pour 4 cm of water into it and cook for 2 10 minutes.

Ketogenic Brownies

Ingredients :

25 g baking cocoa

1/2 teaspoon baking soda

2 pinch (s) of salt

2 pinch (s) of cinnamon

2 pinch (s) of vanilla, fresh

8 0 g almond (s) with shell, ground

25 g butter

25 ml of sunflower oil or coconut oil

40 g xylitol (sugar substitute)

25 g chocolate (Xukkolade), dark chocolate

2 egg (s), separated

Preparation:

1. First, preheat the oven to 300 degrees and separate the eggs.

2. Beat the egg with a little salt, then set it aside.

3. Now melt the butter, oil and xukcolade - this is best done in the microwave.
4. Then mix all the ingredients, except the egg whites, with the butter-chocolate mix and make sure that the mixture is firm too.
5. Then fold in the egg whites and finally fill the whole thing into a tin and let it bake for 28 minutes.

Dark Chocolate Cake

Ingredients :

30 5g dark chocolate (at least 8 0% cocoa content)

270g butter (e.g. from grass-fed cows)

6 eggs (M)

2 pinch of salt (e.g. Azafran pink Himalayan salt from Pakistan)

Preparation:

First preheat the oven to 2 60 degrees, grease a 20-22 cm form and line it with paper.

Now let the chocolate and butter melt and then cool.

Separate the eggs and whip the egg whites with a little salt until stiff.

Then add the egg yolks to the chocolate and stir them together.

Lift the chocolate batter into the egg white and pour it into the mold.

Stick a stick in the middle of the cake to see if it's done. You can tell whether the dough is ready by the fact that nothing sticks to the stick.

Finally, serve cake with lukewarm cream and garnish with berries.

Chocolate Avocado Cake

Ingredients :
270g avocado pulp
65g desiccated coconut
2 6 g cocoa powder
30 g cocoa nibs
65g erythritol
2 00ml coconut milk (unsweetened)
8 6 g ground hazelnuts
30 g chopped hazelnuts

Preparation:
First, grease the shape (2 8cm) and line the bottom with paper.

  Then mix the dry ingredients in a bowl and mix the avocado and coconut milk together.

  Now put the dry ingredients and the dough in the mold and leave everything in the fridge overnight.

26

The next day you have a fantastic result.

Liquid Lava Tartlets

Ingredients :
2 egg
20g dark chocolate (at least 8 0% cocoa content)
30 g butter

Preparation:
First, grease two molds and preheat the oven to 230 degrees.

Now melt the butter and chocolate and let them cool down. Beat the egg until frothy and add the chocolate.

Then spread the dough on the molds and put them in the oven.

Reduce the temperature to 2 8 6 degrees and bake the tarts for 6 minutes. The tartlets should still be liquid inside.

In the last step, take the tartlets out of the molds and cover them with cream.

Blueberry Coconut Ice Cream

Ingredients :

1 teaspoon coconut extract

4 00 g frozen blueberries

85 ml of water

400 ml coconut milk from the refrigerator

6 tbsp powder xucker

1 teaspoon vanilla extract

Preparation:

1. First open the coconut milk and skim off the coconut cream.

2. This is put in a food processor with the powder xucker and coconut extract and everything is whipped to a stiff mass.

3. There should be peaks. If the milk is too firm, you can add 2 tablespoons of coconut water. The berries are mixed and added to the cream.

4. The masses should not be mixed together. So you can get a nice pattern in the cream.
5. This comes in molds (carefully hit a surface 4 times so that there are no air bubbles).
6. The ice cream goes into the freezer for 4 hours. Then serve and enjoy.

Avocado Chocolate Mousse

Ingredients :

2 tbsp cocoa powder

2 tsp cocoa nibs

2 pinch of cinnamon

6 -25 pieces of blueberries

2 tbsp almond flakes

2 pieces of ripe avocado

2 tbsp fresh Lemon juice

2 tbsp chocolate whey (optional - otherwise a little more cocoa)

3-4 tbsp Xucker light

2 pinch of sea salt

Preparation:

Mix all the ingredients, except for the berries and the almond flakes, into a cream and pour into a glass.

  Then decorate the cream with the berries and the leaves and enjoy the delicious avocado chocolate mousse.

Creamy Keto Pudding

Ingredients :

230 g Xucker light

2 pinch of salt

1 pack of gelatine in powder form

6 egg yolks

30 5 g cream (4 0%)

30 5 g almond milk

2 vanilla pod

Preparation:

1. First put the cream and almond milk in a saucepan and heat them up.
2. Then cut the vanilla pod lengthways and scrape out the pulp (you can also use the entire pod).
3. When the cream is boiling add a little sugar and salt and then set everything aside.

4. Then mix the gelatine powder with the rest of the almond milk and let it rest for 10 minutes.
5. Mix the egg yolks and stir in the cream mixture (the egg should not be allowed to stagnate). Then put the mixture back on the stove and stir in the gelatin.
6. When the mixture is thick, remove it from the heat and divide it into 6 bowls.
7. In order for the pudding to set, it must be placed in the refrigerator for a few hours.
8. And the fantastic keto pudding is ready!

Giotto Balls

Ingredients :
45 g Xucker light
25 ml cream (4 0%)
possibly liquid sweetener
possibly a few ground almonds
30 g hazelnuts (chopped nuts)
60 g hazelnut butter
45 g vanilla protein powder

Preparation:
First roast the chopped hazelnuts in oil and then let them cool.

Then mix the remaining ingredients in a bowl and stir them into a malleable mass. Make sure that the mixture does not become too runny and, if necessary, use a little less cream than indicated.

To make the mixture firm, you can fold in ground almonds.

Then roll 20-30   balls out of the mass. Now roll these balls through the chopped hazelnuts to achieve the typical Giotto look. The balls come in the refrigerator for an hour.

Chicken Breast With Pesto And Oven Vegetables

Ingredients:

1 mozzarella

1 spring fresh onion

Salt pepper

230 g chicken breast

1 paprika

2 tomato

2 tbsp tomato pesto

Preparation:

Preheat the oven to 300 degrees. Line a baking sheet with parchment paper or prepare a baking dish.

Chop the vegetables and place them in a small bowl on the baking sheet or pour them into the baking dish. Season the vegetables with salt and pepper.

Briefly wash the chicken breast under cold water and then pat it dry. Carefully cut them into pieces with a sharp knife.

Rub the meat with the tomato pesto. Then cut the fresh mozzarella into slices and place them over the chicken breast pieces. Season everything with salt and pepper.

Either place the chicken breast pieces next to the bowl with the vegetables on the baking sheet or place them in the baking dish directly on top of the vegetables. Bake them together in the oven for about 210 minutes.

Zucchini Cheese Balls

Ingredients:

65g almond flour

25 g coconut flour

Salt pepper

1 zucchini

2 egg

25 g grated parmesan

30 g Gouda cheese

Preparation:

Preheat the oven to 230 degrees and line a baking sheet with parchment paper.

Mix the egg, almond flour, coconut flour, grated Parmesan and Gouda cheese together and season everything with salt and pepper. If the batter becomes too firm, add some water.

Use a food processor to shred the zucchini. Alternatively, you can also use a spiral cutter. Then cut the zucchini into pieces with a small knife.

Add the zucchini to the batter and stir them into the batter.

Form small balls with your hands and place them on the baking sheet.

Bake the balls for about 2 6 -25 minutes. As soon as they turn brown, take them out of the oven and then let them cool.

Tomato Mince Soup

Ingredients:
45g mushrooms
4 cherry tomatoes

Basil

1 teaspoon Italian herbs

Salt pepper

85 g mixed minced meat

1 fresh onion s

1 paprika

2 tbsp cream cheese (light)

65g tomato puree

85 ml vegetable stock

1 tbsp olive oil

1 zucchini

Preparation:

Chop the fresh onion s and sweat them briefly in a pan with olive oil. Add the minced meat and fry it.

Wash the peppers, zucchini, mushrooms, and tomatoes, chop them up, and add them to the ground beef. Fry everything briefly.

Add the tomatoes, cream cheese and oregano to the pan and stir everything together well. Then let the whole thing simmer briefly.

Pour the vegetable stock into the soup and simmer over low heat for about 25 minutes.

Finally, chop the basil and stir it into the soup. Season the soup with salt and pepper.

Pizza And Cheese Roll With Ham

Ingredients:

2 slice of cooked ham

2 spring fresh onion

Arugula

Basil

Salt pepper

10 0g Gouda

10 0g low-fat quark

2 eggs

4 tbsp tomato strains

Preparation:

Preheat the oven to approx. 2 8 0 ° C (with convection) and line a baking sheet with baking paper.

Mix the quark with about two thirds of the cheese and the eggs to form a mass. Season the mixture with a little salt and pepper. Put the mixture on the baking sheet with a spatula and distribute it evenly.

Bake the dough in the middle of the oven for about 2 10 minutes. While the bottom is in the oven, cut the ham into cubes and peel the spring fresh onion . Cut the fresh onion s into rings and season the tomatoes with salt and pepper.

Take the tin with the batter out of the oven and let it cool for a minute. Then brush the dough evenly with the tomato sauce. Spread the ham, spring fresh onion and the rest of the cheese over it and put everything back in the oven for another 25 minutes.

Then take the pizza out of the oven and let it cool down briefly. Then wash the arugula and pour it over the pizza. Then carefully roll the whole thing into a roll and wrap it in aluminum foil.

Zucchini Casserole With Sweet Potato And Mozzarella

Ingredients:
85 g mozzarella (grated)
2 65 ml low-fat milk
2 tbsp olive oil

2 tbsp spelled flour

Nutmeg

2 65 g zucchini

65 g sweet potato

1 spring fresh onion

2 clove of garlic

Parsley

Salt pepper

Preparation:

Wash the zucchini and cut them evenly into slices. Peel the sweet potatoes and cut them into slices as well.

Peel and chop the garlic. Then finely chop the parsley and spring fresh onion .

Heat olive oil in a saucepan and stir in the spelled flour with a whisk. Then slowly add the milk, stirring constantly.

Then add the garlic, parsley, nutmeg, salt and pepper.

Let the zucchini and sweet potatoes simmer briefly in the sauce and then place them in a baking pan.

Bake the whole thing for 45 to 40 minutes at 300 ° C in a preheated oven.

Take the casserole out of the oven and garnish with spring fresh onion s.

Pumpkin Soup With Carrots And Ginger

Ingredients:

4 00 ml of water

2 tbsp olive oil

2 teaspoons of low-fat cream cheese

Salt pepper

1/2 butter squash

2 carrot

1 spring fresh onion

2 cm ginger

Preparation:

Wash the pumpkin thoroughly and cut it in half with a knife. Scoop out the seeds and cut into cubes.

Peel the carrots and spring fresh onion s and cut them into cubes as well. Heat olive oil in a saucepan and sweat the spring fresh onion s in it. Then add the pumpkin and carrots and stir-fry everything.

Deglaze the vegetables with water and cook everything over medium heat for 2 0-2 10 minutes.

Peel the ginger and puree it with a hand blender. Then add it to the soup.

Take the pot off the stove and puree the soup finely with a hand blender. Season everything with salt and pepper and add the cream cheese. Bring everything to the boil again while stirring.

Pumpkin Quinoa

Ingredients:

25 g rocket

Fresh mint

1 lime

2 tbsp olive oil

Salt pepper

45 g quinoa

230 g butter squash

1 fresh onion s

Preparation:

Put the quinoa in a fine sieve and rinse it under running water. Then cook the quinoa in a saucepan with water for about 8 to 25 minutes, until the grains are firm to the bite. Then pour off the water.

Wash the arugula and pumpkin thoroughly and cut the pumpkin in half with a knife. Scoop out the seeds and cut into cubes. Peel the fresh onion and cut it in half. Cut them into thin rings.

Heat some olive oil in the pan and fry the pumpkin pieces in it. Then add the quinoa and fresh onion and season everything with salt and pepper.

Wash the mint and shake it dry. Then pluck the leaves off and cut them into small pieces. Finally add the mint and rocket to the quinoa mixture.

Chicken Skewers With Tzatziki

Ingredients:
250 g of chicken
65 g zucchini
65 g of cocktail tomatoes
45 g paprika
1/2 fresh onion s

2 tbsp olive oil

2 tsp kebab seasoning

60 g Greek yogurt

45 g cucumber

2 clove of garlic

Salt pepper

Preparation:

1. Wash the meat and pat it dry. Cut the meat into pieces.

2. Wash the zucchini and tomatoes and cut them into small pieces. Peel the fresh onion and cut it into pieces as well.

3. Alternate the meat and vegetables on wooden skewers. Add some olive oil, kebab seasoning, and salt and pepper to a small bowl and stir. Then brush the skewers with it.

4. In a pan, grill the skewers evenly on all sides.

5. For the tsatsiki sauce, wash the cucumber and grate it finely. Peel and squeeze the clove of garlic. Then mix the cucumber, garlic, yogurt and a little olive oil with a little salt and pepper and serve the sauce with the meat skewers.

Stuffed Peppers With Cottage Cheese

Ingredients:

Dill

Nutmeg

Salt pepper

2 red peppers

400g of cottage cheese

Coriander

Preparation:

1. Wash the peppers, cut them in half and remove the core.
2. Put all the remaining ingredients in a bowl and mix them together. Season them with nutmeg, salt and pepper.
3. Then pour the mixture into the pepper halves and bake them in the oven for 2 6 minutes at 230 degrees.

Fried Egg And Bacon

Ingredients:

2 eggs

2 handful of rocket

1/2 avocado

4 strips of bacon

Olive oil

Salt pepper

Preparation:

Halve the avocado and remove the stone. Halve half of the avocado again and remove the pulp with a spoon.

Wash the arugula and let it drain well.

Fry the bacon strips in a pan with a little olive oil.

Beat two eggs and bake them in the pan over medium heat next to the bacon strips.

At the end, put all the ingredients together on a plate and season with salt and pepper.

Vegetarian Omelette

Ingredients:

4 eggs

4 cherry tomatoes

1 paprika

1/2 avocado

1 fresh onion s

2 tbsp corn

Parsley

Olive oil

Salt pepper

Preparation:

Wash the peppers, cut them in half and remove the core. Then cut the half into pieces. Halve the avocado and remove the stone.

Halve half of the avocado again and remove the pulp with a spoon. Also, cut half an fresh onion into small pieces.

Wash the parsley and chop it up too. Drain the canned corn in a colander.
Then beat the eggs in a bowl, season the mixture with salt and pepper and whisk it well. Then put the mixture in a pan with olive oil and turn the omelette as soon as it loosens on the bottom of the pan.

After turning it for the first time, spread the vegetables and parsley on the omelette and season it with salt and pepper. Carefully fold it up and take it out of the pan.

Salad Rolls

Ingredients:

1 spring fresh onion

Fresh herbs

Salt pepper

2 fresh sheet of iceberg lettuce

65g lean ham

1/2 paprika

2 tbsp Greek yogurt

Preparation:

For the herb dressing, mix the yogurt with fresh herbs and season with salt and pepper.

Then wash the peppers and cut them into pieces. Peel the spring fresh onion and cut it into rings.

Then wash the lettuce and dry it. Brush it with some herb dressing and place the ham, peppers and fresh onion rings on top.
Roll up the lettuce leaf and secure it with a toothpick.

Colorful Mango And Almond Salad

Ingredients:

2 tbsp water

2 tbsp lime juice

2 tbsp apple cider vinegar

1 teaspoon maple syrup

2 stalk of coriander

1/2 chili pepper

230 g young spinach

230 g of mango pulp

60 g red pepper

25 g almonds

25 g red fresh onion

1 clove of garlic

Salt pepper

Preparation:

For the dressing, cut the mango pulp into cubes. Wash the coriander and shake it dry.

Then pluck the leaves off and chop them up. Then peel the garlic and cut the chilli in half to remove the seeds.

Then put the mango, water, lime juice, apple cider vinegar, maple syrup, chilli pepper and garlic in a blender and puree everything with a hand blender.

Then season the dressing with salt and pepper and add some coriander.

For the salad, wash the spinach leaves and spin dry. Cut the washed pepper into pieces and peel the fresh onion . Then cut the fresh onion into rings.

Then cut the mango pulp into strips and chop the almonds into fresh pieces. Finally, put everything together in a salad bowl and drizzle it with the dressing.

Garlicky Fresh Lemon Mahi-Mahi

You can choose to grill, bake, or sear mahi-mahi. What is more important is that you do what works for you. You can start and finish preparing this meal in about 45 minutes.

Ingredients

- Freshly ground black pepper
- 4 cloves of garlic
- 2 sliced fresh Lemon
- 465g of asparagus
- 4 tablespoons of butter
- Mahi-mahi fillets
- Salt
- Zest fresh Lemon juice
- 2 tablespoon of chopped parsley
- 2 tablespoons of extra virgin oil

Method of preparation

- Melt butter and olive oil over medium heat.
- Add mahi-mahi and season with salt and pepper.
- Cook until it turns golden, then turn it to the other side.
- Transfer it to a plate.
- For the skillet, add 2 tablespoon of oil, then add asparagus and cook for 4 minutes.
- Season it with salt and pepper then transfer it to a clean plate.
- Also, add 2 tablespoons of butter to the skillet and after melting, add chili flakes and garlic.
- Cook for 2 minute before adding zest, lemon, and parsley.
- Remove the mixture from heat and return the asparagus and mahi-mahi to the skillet.
- Garnish it with parsley before serving.

Philly Cheesesteak Lettuce Wraps

Ingredients

- Freshly ground pepper
- 2 tablespoons of vegetable oil
- 2 tablespoon of freshly chopped parsley
- Salt
- 465g of skirt steak
- 2 teaspoon of dried oregano
- 2 fresh fresh onion
- 8 fresh lettuce leaves.

Method of preparation

- Place a fresh pan over medium heat.
- Add 2 tablespoon of oil, fresh onion , bell pepper, oregano, salt, and pepper.
- Cook and stir until the vegetables are soft.
- Remove the pepper and fresh onion from the pan and heat the remaining oil.

- Add steak in one layer and season with salt and pepper. Cook until the steak is seared on one side before flipping to the other side. Cook it for about 2 minutes, then add fresh onion mixture to the pan and combine it.
- Sprinkle provolone and fresh onion s then cover the pan with a tight lid. Cook it until the cheese melts before removing from heat.
- Arrange the lettuce and scoop the steak mixture on each piece of lettuce. Garnish it with parsley and serve cold or warm.

Creamy Garlic Butter Tuscan Shrimp

Ingredients

- 2 tablespoon of fresh parsley
- 2 small yellow fresh onion
- 2 tablespoons of salted butter
- 2 pound of shrimp, salt, pepper
- 1 cup of white wine
- 4 cups of spinach leaves
- 2/4 cup of fresh parmesan cheese
- 2 teaspoons of dried Italian herbs
- 2 teaspoon of cornstarch, and sun-dried tomato strips.

Method of preparation

- Heat skillet over medium heat.
- Melt the butter and add garlic. Fry the mixture for about one minute, then add shrimp and fry for two minutes on each side.
- Transfer it into another bowl and set aside.

61

- Fry the fresh onion in the butter that remains in the skillet and pour the optional white wine. Allow it to reduce to half and scrape any bits at the bottom of the pan.
- Add the dried tomatoes and fry to 3-4 minutes.
- Reduce the heat to low and add the mixture while gently stirring it.
- Season with salt and pepper before introducing spinach leaves and parmesan cheese in the sauce.
- Add shrimp to the pan, then sprinkle parsley leaves and stir again.
- Serve with rice or pasta.

Keto Chicken Soup

Ingredients

2 cloves of minced garlic

1/2 cup of chopped fresh onion s

8 ounces of cauliflower

1 teaspoon of paprika

1/2 cup of chopped fresh onion s

2 stalks of chopped celery

2 tablespoons of avocado oil

2 pound of boneless chicken thighs.

Method of preparation

- Heat the oil in a saucepan over medium heat.
- Add fresh onion s and celery and season with pepper and salt.
- Cook while frequently stirring until the vegetables are tender.
- Add thyme, garlic, and paprika until it is fragrant.
- Stir until it starts boiling.

- Add cauliflower and chicken and reduce the heat. Cook until the chicken and cauliflower are tender.
- Ensure that you use the appropriate amount of salt and pepper.

Keto Burger Buns

Ingredients

- 4 tablespoons of almond flour
- 2 egg
- 2 .6 tablespoons of oil
- 1 teaspoons of baking powder.

Method of preparation

1. Get a small bowl and mix your baking powder and almond flour thoroughly to ensure there are no clumps.
2. Add oil and egg, then beat it like you're making an omelet.
3. Use a fork to get all the lumps out and whip it to get maximum fluff.
4. Microwave the mixture on high heat for 10 0 seconds.
5. After 10 0 seconds, you would see a bun at the bottom of the bowl. It would slightly pull away from the bowl when it is done.

6. Remove it from the bowl and let it cool before slicing.

Parmesan Egg Toast With Tomatoes

- 1 teaspoon salt
- 2 fresh eggs
- 2 tablespoon shredded Parmesan cheese
- 2 Slices reduced-calorie whole wheat toast

- 1 teaspoon chopped garlic (about 2 clove)
- 2 teaspoon olive oil
- 6 cherry tomatoes, quartered
- 1/2 teaspoon freshly ground black pepper

Preparations

1. In a small skillet, preheat the oil over medium heat. Add the tomatoes and garlic into the pan and sauté for 2 minutes, stirring constantly. Season with

salt and pepper and transfer to a plate to heat.

2. In the same pan, brown the eggs for 2 minutes. Flip and cook to desired point (45 seconds for very easy, 2 minute for medium, 2 minutes for very good).

3. Place one egg on the slices of toast, top with half the tomatoes and sprinkle with half the Parmesan.

Greek Breakfast Wraps

Ingredients

- 1 cup fresh baby spinach leaves
- 2 teaspoon olive oil
- 2 tablespoon fresh basil
- 1 teaspoon salt
- 4 egg whites, beaten
- 1/2 teaspoon freshly ground black pepper
- 2 (8-inch) whole wheat tortillas
- 1/2 cup crumbed low-fat feta cheese

Preparation

1. In a small skillet, preheat the oil over medium heat. Add the basil and spinach to the pan and sauté for about 2 minutes or until the spinach wilts.

2. Add the egg whites to the pan, season with salt and pepper and sauté, stirring constantly, for another two minutes or until the egg whites are firm.

3. Remove from heat and sprinkle with feta cheese.

4. Microwave tortillas for 25 to 45 seconds, or until tender and warm. Divide the eggs between the tortillas and wrap them in a burrito style.

Curried Chicken Breast Wraps

30 5 calories per serving

These quick and filling wraps deliver lots of flavor with very few calories. Make the filling ahead of time to have on hand for work lunches and busy days.

Ingredients

- 2 tablespoons plain low-fat yogurt
- 6 ounces cooked chicken breast, cubed
- 2 teaspoon Dijon mustard
- 2 small Gala or Granny Smith apple, cored and chopped
- 1 teaspoon mild curry powder
- 2 cup spring lettuce mix or baby lettuce
- 2 (8-inch) whole wheat tortillas

Preparations

1. In a small bowl, combine the yogurt, chicken, Dijon mustard and curry powder; mix well to combine. Add the apple and mix well.

2. Divide the lettuce between the tortillas and add the chicken mixture to each half. Wrap in a burrito shape and serve.

Protein Power Sweet Potatoes

Ingredients

- 1 teaspoon salt
- 2 medium sweet potatoes
- 1/2 teaspoon freshly ground black pepper
- 1/2 Cup dried cranberries
- 6 ounces plain Greek yogurt

Preparations

1. Preheat the oven to 400ºF and pierce the sweet potatoes a few times with a fork. Put it on a baking sheet then bake for 40 to 46 minutes or until they bite easily with a fork.

2. Cut the potatoes in half and pour the pulp into a medium bowl, keeping the skins intact. Add salt, pepper, yogurt and cranberries to the bowl and mix well with a fork.

3. Pour the mixture into the potato skin and serve hot.

Baked Salmon Fillets With Tomato And Mushrooms

Ingredients

- 2 teaspoons olive oil, divided
- 2 (4-ounce) skin-on salmon fillets
- 1 teaspoon salt
- 1 teaspoon chopped fresh dill
- 1/2 teaspoon freshly ground black pepper
- 1 cup diced fresh tomato
- 1 cup sliced fresh mushrooms

Preparations

1. Preheat the oven to 490 ºF and line a baking sheet with foil.
2. Making use of a pastry brush or your fingers, coat both sides of the fillets with 1 teaspoon of olive oil each. Place the salmon skin face down in the pan.
3. Sprinkle evenly with salt and pepper.

4. In a bowl, combine the remaining teaspoon of olive oil, dill, tomato and mushrooms; mix well to combine. Pour the mixture over the fillets.

5. Fold the foil sides and ends to seal the fish, place the pan on the middle oven rack and bake it for about 25 minutes or until the salmon comes off easily.

Avocado And Fennel Salad With Balsamic Vinaigrette

Ingredients

- 2 tablespoon balsamic vinegar
- 2 tablespoon light olive oil
- 1/2 teaspoon salt
- 1 avocado, diced
- 1 cup fennel, sliced
- 1 cup mandarin oranges, drained
- 1/2 teaspoon freshly ground black pepper
- 2 cup chopped romaine lettuce

Preparation

1. Combine balsamic vinegar, olive oil, pepper and salt in a small bowl and beat until smooth and slightly thickened. Here is your balsamic vinaigrette.

2. Add the fennel, avocado, orange and lettuce; stir until vegetables are well coated with seasoning. Divide between two salad plates and serve cold.

Hearty Shrimp And Kale Soup

Ingredients

- 2 Cloves garlic
- 2 teaspoon olive oil
- 1/2 cup chopped fresh onion
- 2 cup thinly sliced fresh carrots
- 2 Cups chopped fresh kale
- 1 teaspoon salt
- 8 medium (4 6–40 count) raw shrimp, peeled and halved
- 2 1 cups vegetable stock
- 2 cup canned great northern beans, drained
- 1/2 teaspoon freshly ground black pepper
- 1/2 cup chopped fresh parsley

Preparations

1. Heat the oil over little heat in a small saucepan. Add the garlic, fresh onion , cabbage and carrots and sauté for 6 minutes, stirring constantly.

2. Season the veggies with pepper and salt and add the vegetable broth. Cook uncovered for 45 minutes or until carrots are tender.

3. Increase the heat and let the soup boil. Add the shrimp and cook 2 minutes or until the shrimp are pink and slightly firm. Reduce the heat.

4. Use a fork to knead about a quarter of the beans. Mix all the beans in the soup and add the parsley. Cook 2 minutes or until completely hot.

5. Put the ladle into the bowls and serve hot.

Penne Pasta With Vegetables

Ingredients

- ¾ cup uncooked penne pasta
- 2 teaspoon salt, divided
- 2 tablespoon olive oil
- 2 teaspoon chopped fresh oregano
- 2 tablespoon chopped garlic
- 2 cup sliced fresh mushrooms
- 2 cup fresh spinach leaves
- 25 cherry tomatoes, halved
- 1 teaspoon freshly ground black pepper
- 2 tablespoon shredded Parmesan cheese

Preparations

1. In a medium saucepan, bring one liter of water to a boil. Add 1 teaspoon of salt and penne and cook according to package directions or al dente (about 10 minutes). Drain, but do not rinse the penne, reserving about 1/2 cup of water for the pasta.

2. Meanwhile, in a fresh skillet, heat the oil over medium-high heat. Add the garlic, oregano and mushrooms and sauté for 4 to 6 minutes or until the mushrooms are golden brown.

3. Add the season, tomatoes and spinach with the remaining 1 teaspoon of salt and pepper and sauté for three to four mins or until the spinach wilts.

4. Add the drained pasta to the pot, as well as 2-4 tablespoons of water for the pasta. Cook, stirring continuously, two to three mins or until the dough is shiny and the water is cooked through.

5. Divide the dough into two shallow bowls and sprinkle with Parmesan cheese. Serve hot or at room temperature.

Pork Loin Chops With Mango Salsa

Ingredients

- 1 cup lime juice
- 2 pork loin chops, ¾ inch thick
- Juice of 2 fresh orange
- 1 cup diced green bell pepper
- 2 fresh ripe mango, peeled and diced
- 1 cup diced red bell pepper
- 2 tablespoon chopped fresh cilantro
- 2 small jalapeño pepper, seeded and diced
- 1 cup diced red fresh onion
- 1 teaspoon salt
- 2 tbn chopped fresh parsley
- 1/2 tbn freshly ground black pepper

Preparations

1. Place the pork chops in the freezer and add the fresh Lemon and orange juice. Seal, shake to mix well and refrigerate overnight.

2. In a bowl, combine the mango, red fresh onion , peppers, jalapeño, cilantro and parsley. Stir to mix well. Cover and refrigerate overnight.

3. Preheat broiler and line a baking sheet of aluminum foil.

4. Season the pork chops on each sides with pepper and salt. Put in the pot and cook 4-6 minutes on one side, turn and cook another 4-10 minutes. Place the pork chops on a different plate, drizzle with sauce and serve.

Spinach And Swiss Cheese Omelette

Ingredients
- 6 fresh egg whites, beaten
- 2 teaspoon olive oil
- 2 cup fresh baby spinach leaves
- 1/2 teaspoon freshly ground black pepper
- 1 teaspoon salt
- 2 (2 -ounce) slices reduced-fat Swiss cheese

Preparations
1. Preheat the oil over high heat in a small skillet. Add the spinach, salt and pepper and brown for 4 minutes, stirring constantly.
2. Use a spatula to spread the spinach evenly over the bottom of the pan and pour the egg whites on top, tilting the pan to completely cover the spinach.

3. Cook for 4 -4 minutes, occasionally pulling the edges of the eggs towards the center while tilting the saucepan to allow the raw egg to spread over the edges of the pan.

4. When the center of the eggs is almost (but not completely) dry, use a spatula to turn the eggs. Place the Swiss cheese slices in one half of the omelet and turn the other half to form a half moon. Cook until cheese is melted and heated through.

5. To serve, cut the omelet in half and serve hot.

Lemon-Sesame Chicken And Asparagus

230 calories per serving

Chicken and asparagus go together well, and this recipe combines them with a hint of fresh Lemon and the added crunch of sesame seeds.

Ingredients

- 1 cup plus 2 tablespoon fresh Lemon juice, divided
- 8 ounces skinless chicken breast tenders (or quartered chicken breast)
- 2 teaspoon chopped fresh rosemary
- 1 teaspoon olive oil
- 6 medium spears fresh asparagus, cut into 2-inch pieces
- 2 teaspoon salt, divided
- 2 tablespoons sesame seeds
- 1/2 teaspoon freshly ground black pepper

Preparations

1. Beat the chicken slices with a hammer or the palm of your hand until they are evenly 1 inch thick. Place in the freezer with 1 cup of fresh Lemon juice and marinate for 2 hours or overnight.

2. Preheat grill and line a baking sheet of aluminum foil.

3. Season the chicken on both sides with 1 teaspoon of salt and pepper and place in the pan. Sprinkle with rosemary.

4. In a small bowl, season the asparagus with the oil, the remaining tablespoon of fresh Lemon juice and the remaining 1 teaspoon of salt. Arrange the asparagus around the chicken in the pan.

5. Grill the chicken for 4 to 6 minutes, turn it over and add the asparagus and cook for another 4 to 10 minutes.

6. Divide the chicken and asparagus between two plates and sprinkle with the sesame seeds.

Grilled Chicken Salad With Poppy Seed Sauce

Ingredients

- 2 tablespoon apple cider vinegar
- 2 tablespoons light olive oil
- 2 teaspoon Dijon mustard
- 1 cup chopped cooked chicken breast
- 2 tablespoon poppy seeds
- 2 cup chopped romaine lettuce
- 2 medium red bell pepper, chopped
- 2 medium unpeeled cucumber, sliced
- 2 small red fresh onion , chopped

Preparations

1. In a bowl, combine Dijon mustard, olive oil, apple cider vinegar and poppy seeds for about 2 minute or until combined and well blended.

2. Add the chicken, lettuce, cucumber, peppers and fresh onion s and mix well until smooth.

3. Divide between two salad plates and serve immediately.

Toasted Pepper Jack Sandwiches

Ingredients

- 4 slices reduced-calorie whole wheat bread
- 2 Slices reduced-calorie pepper jack cheese
- 1 cup fresh arugula leaves
- 4 thin slices fresh tomato

Preparations

1. Preheat the oven to 4 65 degrees F.
2. Place one slice of cheese on the 2 slices of bread; decorate each with 2 slices of tomato and half of the arugula. Cover with the rest of the slices of bread and place the buns on a baking sheet in the center of the oven.

3. Broil for 4 minutes, then flip and toast for an additional 2-4 minutes, or until bread is golden and cheese is melted. Cut each loaf in half to serve.

Broiled Halibut With Garlic Spinach

Ingredients

- 1 fresh Lemon (about 2 teaspoon juice)
- 2 (4-ounce) halibut fillets, 2 inch thick
- 2 teaspoon salt, divided
- 1 teaspoon cayenne pepper
- 1/2 teaspoon freshly ground black pepper
- 2 teaspoon olive oil
- 1 cup chopped red fresh onion
- 2 Cloves garlic
- 2 Cups fresh baby spinach leave

Preparation

1. Preheat the grill and place an oven rack 5 to 10 inches below the heat source. Line a baking sheet with foil.

2. Squeeze half the fresh Lemon over the fish fillets and season each side with 1 teaspoon of salt, pepper and cayenne pepper. Place the fish in the pan and grill for 8 -8 minutes. Flip the fish and grill for another 6 to 8 minutes or until chipped.

3. Meanwhile, heat the oil in a skillet. Add the garlic and fresh onion then sauté for 2 minutes. Add the spinach and the remaining 1 teaspoon of salt and sauté for another 2 minutes. Remove from heat then cover to keep warm.

4. To serve, divide the spinach into two plates and decorate each serving with a fish fillet. Serve hot.

Quick Miso Soup With Shrimp And Bok Choy

Ingredients

- 8 fresh (4 4–40 count) raw shrimp, peeled and halved
- 2 Cups water
- 2 cup chopped bok choy
- 2 cup cubed firm tofu
- 1/2 cup white miso paste
- 2 green fresh onion s, chopped

Preparations

1. In a saucepan, boil the water over high heat. Add the shrimp and allow to boil for one minute.
2. Reduce the heat and add the bok choy. Cook for 2 minutes, then add the miso and tofu. Cook for another minute.
3. To serve, divide into two bowls and sprinkle with chives.

Quinoa With Sweet Potatoes And Curried Black Beans

Ingredients

- 2 cup water
- 1 cup quinoa
- 1 cup diced and peeled sweet potato (about 2 small)
- 1 teaspoon dried rosemary
- 1 teaspoon olive oil
- 2 cup canned black beans, drained
- 2 tablespoons chopped fresh parsley
- 2 teaspoon mild curry powder

Preparations

1. Wash the quinoa under cold running water through a fine mesh sieve.
2. Drain well on absorbent paper then dry.

3. In a small saucepan, toast the quinoa for 5 minutes over medium heat, stirring constantly.

4. Add the water, heat and let it boil.

5. Cover, reduce heat and cook 2 6 minutes or until it as quinoa is plump and the germ as small spirals in each grain.

6. Remove from heat then cover to keep warm.

7. In a small bowl, season the sweet potatoes with olive oil and rosemary.

8. Transfer to a medium skillet over medium-high heat. Sauté, stirring constantly, for 6 to 8 minutes or until well caramelized.

9. Add the black beans and curry powder, reduce the heat to medium and cook, stirring constantly, until the beans are heated through.

10. To serve, place 1 cup of cooked quinoa on each plate and top with half the bean mixture. Garnish with parsley

Salmon And Tomato Egg Sandwiches

This sandwich breakfast is much healthier and more important than all that you can pick up at the drive-through; It is also very tasty, but it only takes a few minutes to prepare.

Ingredients

- 2 teaspoon olive oil
- 4 light multigrain English muffins
- 6 ounces canned pink salmon
- 8 fresh eggs, beaten
- 2 cup diced tomatoes
- 1 teaspoon salt
- 2 cup fresh arugula

- 1/2 teaspoon freshly ground black pepper

Preparations

1. Toast English muffins while preparing eggs.

2. In a skillet, heat the oil. Add the salmon and tomatoes to the pan and sauté, stirring constantly, for 4 minutes.

3. Pour over eggs, season with salt and pepper and stir, stirring constantly, for about 2 minutes or until eggs solidify.

4. Place English muffin halves on 4 plates and cover each bottom half with a quarter of the egg mixture. Complete with the rocket and the other half of the muffin.

Nutty Peach Parfaits

These parfaits may look good, but are also healthier than they look. The walnuts add omega-4 fats and fiber as well as crunch, and the Greek yogurt has as much as fourteen grams of protein per cup.

Ingredients

- 4 (6-ounce) containers vanilla Greek yogurt
- 4 medium peaches, sliced
- 1 cup unsalted walnuts, chopped

Preparation

1. Divide the ingredients between four parfaits or desserts. Start with a layer of peaches; then add a spoonful of yogurt and a pinch of walnuts.

Cocoa-Banana Breakfast Smoothie

This smoothie only takes seconds to prepare, but is packed with healthy nutrients. Greek yogurt provides a dose of protein, and bananas are a great source of potassium.

Ingredients

- 2 medium bananas, cut into chunks
- 24 ounces vanilla Greek yogurt
- 2 teaspoon honey
- 1 cup low-fat milk
- 2 tablespoons unsweetened cocoa powder
- 1 cup ice cubes

Preparation

1. Place the yogurt and bananas in a blender and blend until smooth. Add honey, cocoa and milk and beat again until combined.

2. Add ice and beat again, pulsing as needed, until smooth and thick

Scrambled Egg Soft Tacos

Finding fast food alternatives for your morning meal can be difficult, but this recipe is great to try. It's packed with Southwestern flavors, but low in fat and calories.

Ingredients

- 2 teaspoon olive oil
- 8 (6-inch) whole wheat tortillas
- 2 green fresh onion s, chopped
- 2 2 fresh eggs, beaten
- 1 teaspoon cayenne pepper
- 2 cup mild chunky salsa
- 2 cup low-fat shredded cheddar cheese

Preparations

1. Put the tortillas on a plate, then cover with a damp paper towel and microwave for about one mins, or until warm and supple. Cover with a second dish or a pan lid to keep them warm.

2. In a big, heavy-bottomed pan, heat the oil over medium heat. Add the chives and sauté for 2 minute. Add the cayenne pepper to the eggs and place them in the pan. Stir, stirring constantly, until eggs are cooked through, about 10 minutes.

3. Divide the egg mixture evenly between the tortillas, decorate the tortillas with 2 tablespoons of salsa and cheddar cheese and fold the tacos in half.

Cranberry-Walnut Whole Wheat Pancakes

These pancakes are a delightful way to start the day. Blueberries are sour, but sweet, and the nuts add crunch and texture to this comfort classic.

Ingredients

- ¾ cup whole wheat flour
- 1 cup fresh cranberries
- 2 tablespoons sugar
- 1/2 teaspoon salt
- 2 tablespoon baking powder
- 1 teaspoon ground nutmeg
- 2 1/2 cup low-fat milk
- 1 teaspoon pure vanilla extract
- 2 fresh egg, beaten
- 2 tablespoon coconut oil, divided
- 1 cup chopped walnuts

Preparations

1. In a bowl, toss the cranberries with a handful of wholemeal flour, turning them well to coat.

2. In a bowl, combine the remaining flour, sugar, baking powder, salt and nutmeg, stirring to combine well.

3. Add the egg, vanilla, milk and mix well, but without stirring too much. The dough should remain a little uneven. Gently mix the nuts and cranberries (with the flour) and set the dough aside for 25 minutes.

4. In a large, heavy-bottomed pan, heat about 1 teaspoon of coconut oil over medium heat. Mix enough batter in the pan to make a 6 inch pancake. Cook until the edges are bubbling, then flip the pancake and cook for another minute. Transfer to a plate then

cover it to keep warm while making the rest of the pancakes. Add extra coconut oil to the pan as needed.

5. To serve, place 2 pancakes on each plate and decorate with hot maple syrup, honey or molasses.

Herb And Swiss Frittata

This frittata looks like something you'd see in a restaurant, but it only takes a few minutes to get ready. You'll love the layered flavors, thanks to the sweet Swiss cheese and fresh herbs.

Ingredients

- 8 fresh eggs, beaten
- 2 teaspoons olive oil
- 1 teaspoon salt
- 2 teaspoons chopped fresh parsley
- 1 teaspoon freshly ground black pepper
- 2 teaspoons chopped fresh marjoram
- 1 cup shredded low-fat Swiss cheese
- 2 teaspoon chopped fresh basil

Preparation

1. Preheat the oven to 4 8 6 degrees F.

2. Heat oil on a fresh baking sheet over high heat. Pour the eggs, distributing them evenly on the baking sheet. Season with salt and pepper.

3. Take down the pan from the heat and sprinkle the parsley, marjoram and basil evenly over the eggs. Cover with Swiss cheese.

4. Place the pan in the oven center and bake for 2 8 to 30 minutes or until a toothpick you inserted in the center is clean.

5. To serve, cut into four slices and serve hot.

Scrambled Eggs With Mushrooms And Fresh Onion S

This egg dish cooks fast, but has a flavor that will require you to take it slowly and taste it. It's also a great sandwich filling. If you must grab your breakfast on the go, a whole pita pocket is a good choice.

Ingredients

- 2 cup sliced fresh mushrooms
- 2 teaspoon olive oil
- 1/2 cup thinly sliced yellow fresh onion
- 1 cup chopped fresh parsley
- 2 tablespoon chopped fresh tarragon
- 1 teaspoon salt
- 8 fresh eggs, beaten
- 1 teaspoon freshly ground black pepper

Preparations

1. In a heavy-bottomed pan, heat the oil. Add the mushrooms, fresh onion , tarragon, parsley, salt and pepper and sauté for 4 minutes, stirring occasionally.

2. Pour in the eggs and stir, stirring constantly, until cooked through, about 2 minutes. To serve, divide into 4 plates.

Vanilla-Almond Protein Shake

This breakfast shake contains lots of healthy proteins and fats to keep you going on even your toughest mornings. It's a great way to make breakfast - just pour it into a travel mug and drink it on the go

Ingredients

- 4 scoops unflavored whey protein isolate powder
- 2 Cups cold water
- 1/2 cup almond butter
- 1 teaspoon almond extract
- 2 tablespoons honey
- 1 teaspoon ground nutmeg
- 25 ice cubes

Preparations

1. In a blender, combine cold water, protein powder, almond butter, honey, almond extract, and nutmeg. Beat over high heat

for about 45 seconds or until smooth.

2. Add ice cubes and beat again until thick and creamy. Drink immediately.

Grilled Fruit Salad

Fruits don't always have to be raw; in fact, toasting or grilling fresh fruit enhances its natural sugars and enhances its flavor. Duplicate the recipe and use the leftovers as a side dish for chicken or seafood.

Ingredients

- 4 fresh peaches or nectarines, pitted and sliced into 8 pieces each
- 8 slices fresh or canned (unsweetened) pineapple
- 8 (½- inch-thick) slices fresh honeydew melon
- 1 teaspoon salt
- 2 teaspoon honey, warmed for 45 seconds in microwave

Preparations

1. Preheat the grill then line a baking sheet with foil.

2. Spread the fruit in one single layer on the baking sheet and brush with honey on both sides. Sprinkle salt on top and place the pan 4 cm under the grill.

3. Cook 4 minutes, turn each piece of fruit and cook for another 2 minutes, or until the fruit is somewhat browned around the edges.

4. Place 2 pineapple slices, 8 peach slices and 2 melon slices on each of the 4 plates and serve hot.

Easy Granola Bars

This recipe is much greater for you than any other commercial cereal bars, which are often laden with less healthy grains and high-fructose corn syrup. These bars baked up in a snap and can be stored in an airtight container for up to a week, or if they last that long.

Ingredients

- 2 cup pecan pieces
- 2 teaspoon coconut oil
- 2 cup raw pumpkin seeds
- 2 cup dried cranberries
- 2 cup chopped walnuts
- 2 cup dried apricots, chopped
- 1/2 cup coconut oil, melted
- 2 cup unsweetened coconut flakes
- 1 cup almond butter
- 1/2 teaspoon pure vanilla extract
- 2 teaspoon ground cinnamon
- 1 cup raw honey

- 1 teaspoon salt

Preparations

1. Preheat the oven to 4 30   ºF. Grease a 10 by 2 4 -inch baking dish with 2 teaspoon of coconut oil and set aside.

2. In a fresh bowl, combine walnuts, pumpkin seeds, walnuts, cranberries, apricots, and coconut flakes and mix well.

3. In a pan, mix the melted coconut oil, almond butter, honey, vanilla, salt and cinnamon and heat until the honey is melted.

4. Transfer the nut mixture into the baking sheet, pressing down to distribute it evenly. Pour the honey mixture calmly over the top.

5. Bake until golden brown (40 to 46 mins). Allow the mixture to cool to room temperature before

cutting it into equal bars. Store in an airtight vessel for up to 2 week.

Hearty Hot Cereal With Berries

Whole grains aren't only good for your heart; they are also perfect for your life. The content which is high in fiber makes them filling and provides a slow and sustained energy for your day. The addition of red fruits and nuts to this recipe makes it particularly satisfying.

Ingredients

- 1 teaspoon salt
- 4 cups water
- 2 tablespoons honey
- 2 Cups whole rolled oats
- 1 cup fresh blueberries
- 1 cup fresh raspberries
- 2 cup low-fat milk
- 1 cup chopped walnuts
- 2 teaspoons flaxseed

Preparations

1. In a saucepan, boil the water over high heat and add salt.

2. Add the oats, nuts and flax seeds, reduce the heat and cover. Cook for 25 minutes or until oats reach desired consistency.

3. Divide the oats among 4 deep bowls and cover each with 2 tablespoons of blueberries and raspberries. Add 1/2 cup of milk to each bowl and serve.

Pecan-Banana Pops

A healthy breakfast doesn't have to be hot; in fact, this one is frozen. Make a few of these pops ahead of time and keep them in the freezer. They are also a great after school gift. Kids love them!

Ingredients

- 2 tablespoons raw honey
- 4 fresh just-ripe bananas
- 4 Popsicle sticks
- ¾ cup chopped pecans
- 1 cup almond butter

Preparations

1. Peel and cut one end of each banana and insert a popsicle stick into the cut end.

2. In a bowl, mix the almond butter and honey and heat in the microwave for until the mixture is slightly diluted. Pour over a sheet of baking paper

or aluminum foil and spread with a spatula.

3. On another piece of parchment paper or plastic wrap, spread the chopped nuts. Line a plate or sheet with a third piece of parchment paper or plastic wrap.

4. Wrap each banana first in the honey mixture until well coated, then in the nuts until completely coated, pressing gently so that the nuts stick together.

5. Place each ready-made banana on the baking sheet. When all the bananas are covered, place the dough in the freezer for at least 2 hours. For long-term storage, transfer the frozen bananas to a resealable plastic bag.

Tuna And Bean Salad Pockets

This light yet hearty recipe is perfect for workday lunches. It packs well and tastes better because you have the option of sitting down, so make your salad the night before and put it in your pita pocket, then in your lunch box in the morning.

Ingredients

- 2 (6-ounce) can tuna filled in water, drained
- 4 whole wheat pita pockets
- 1 (2 6 -ounce) can pinto beans, rinsed and drained
- 2 tablespoons light mayonnaise
- 1/2 cup diced white fresh onion
- 2 teaspoon spicy brown mustard
- 1 teaspoon freshly ground black pepper
- 1 teaspoon celery seed
- 2 cup chopped romaine lettuce

Preparations

119

1. If the rolls are not sliced, cut them so that there is a pocket-like opening, being careful not to cut the sides or the bottom.
2. In a small bowl, combine the tuna, borlotti beans, fresh onion , mayonnaise, mustard, celery and pepper; mix well.
3. Divide the lettuce among the pita pockets and top each with a quarter of the tuna salad.

Shrimp And Cranberry Salad

Dried cranberries add a tangy touch of flavor to   this fresh shrimp salad. Using steamed shrimp from your seafood counter makes this a really quick lunch to make.

Ingredients

- 1 cup sliced red fresh onion
- 2   dozen fresh (30 –45 count) cooked shrimp, peeled and deveined
- 1/2 cup lime juice
- 1/2 teaspoon paprika
- 1/2 teaspoon ground cumin
- 2 Cups chopped romaine lettuce
- 1 orange bell pepper, chopped
- 1 yellow bell pepper, chopped
- 1/2 cup dried cranberries
- 1/2 cup of your favorite homemade or store-bought balsamic vinaigrette

Preparations

1. In a small bowl, season the shrimp with the fresh Lemon juice, cumin and paprika and let stand 45 minutes in the refrigerator. Then drain.
2. In a fresh bowl, combine lettuce, fresh onion , peppers and cranberries until smooth.
3. Add the marinated shrimp and balsamic vinaigrette and toss again. Divide among 4 salad plates and serve.

Chicken Breast With Roasted Summer Veggies

This recipe reheats really well, so make it on the weekend or at night and wrap it in individual containers to take out for lunch during the week. Experiment with other seasonal vegetables to vary the flavors.

Ingredients

- 2 tbn plus 2 teaspoon olive oil, divided
- 4 (4-to 6 -ounce) skinless chicken breasts
- 2 teaspoon salt, divided
- 1 teaspoon ground turmeric
- 1 teaspoon freshly ground black pepper, divided
- 2 medium zucchini, thinly sliced
- 2 medium white fresh onion , sliced 1 inch thick
- 2 yellow squash, thinly sliced
- 2 pint cherry tomatoes
- 2 teaspoon dried oregano

- 2 teaspoon dried parsley

Preparations

1. Preheat the oven to 400ºF and line a baking pan with aluminum foil.

2. Rub each sides of the chicken breasts with 2 teaspoon of the olive oil and season them with 1 teaspoon of the salt, 1/2 teaspoon of the pepper, and the turmeric. Place the chicken on the pan.

3. In a bowl, combine the squash, zucchini, fresh onion , and tomatoes. Add the parsley and oregano and then drizzle with the remaining 2 tablespoon olive oil. Toss the vegetables well until they are evenly coated, and spread around the chicken breasts on the pan.

124

4. Bake in the oven center for 2 6 minutes, turn over the chicken and stir the vegetables, and then bake for 2 2 minutes more, or until the chicken juices run clear.

5. To serve, place 2 breast on each plate and top with one-quarter of the vegetables.

Seafood-Stuffed Avocadoes

This is a great light lunch, especially during the warmer months. You can prepare the filling up to three days ahead and just assemble the dish when you're ready to eat.

Ingredients

- 2 cup cooked cocktail shrimp
- 2 tablespoons light mayonnaise
- 8 ounces imitation flaked crabmeat, chopped
- 2 tablespoon plain yogurt
- 2 stalk celery, finely chopped
- 1 red bell pepper, chopped
- 1 red fresh onion , chopped
- 2 SCallions, sliced
- 1/2 teaspoon dry mustard
- 2 tablespoons chopped fresh parsley
- 1 teaspoon freshly ground black pepper
- 2 avocados

- 2 teaspoon fresh Lemon juice

Preparations

1. In a mixing bowl, combine the shrimp, crabmeat, celery, bell pepper, fresh onion , and scallions; mix well.

2. In a bowl, combine the yogurt, mayonnaise, dry mustard, parsley, and black pepper, and stir with a fork until well combined.

3. Combine the mayonnaise mixture with the seafood filling until well blended.

4. Cut the avocados into half, remove the pits, and wipe the flesh with the fresh Lemon juice. Fill each avocado half with one-quarter of the seafood filling and serve.

Easy Chicken Pasta Soup

Boil the pasta a day or two ahead of time and after draining, place it in a resealable bag in the fridge until it is ready to use. This bit of prep work Makes this soup a lunch that takes just ten minutes to make.

Ingredients

- 4 Cups chicken stock
- 2 cup frozen green beans
- 2 cup frozen sliced carrots
- 2 (6-ounce) can flaked chicken, drained
- 2 teaspoon chopped fresh tarragon
- 2 teaspoon fresh thyme leaves
- 1 teaspoon salt
- 1/2 teaspoon freshly ground black pepper
- 2 cup cooked mini-shell pasta
- 1 cup shredded Parmesan cheese

Preparations

1. In a pan, boil the chicken stock over high heat. Add the green beans and carrots, and reduce the heat to medium. Cover and let simmer for 10 minutes.

2. Add the chicken, tarragon, thyme, salt, and pepper, and simmer for 4 minutes more. Put down the pan from the heat and stir in the cooked pasta.

3. To serve, divide between 4 bowls and top with the Parmesan.

Chopped Blt Salad

This salad lets you enjoy all the flavors of the classic BLT sandwich without going overboard on fat and calories. Using turkey bacon and croutons (instead of bread) go a long way toward making this a healthier way to have a BLT.

Ingredients

- 4 slices turkey bacon
- 2 Cups chopped iceberg lettuce
- 2 medium tomatoes, diced
- 1 cup plain croutons
- 2 tablespoon mayonnaise
- 2 tablespoon light Italian dressing

Preparations

1. Prepare the turkey bacon in the microwave according to package directions. Allow it to drain on paper towels and cool for 10 minutes.

2. Meanwhile, combine the lettuce, tomatoes, and croutons in a fresh bowl.
3. In a small cup, stir together the mayonnaise and Italian dressing (it will be thick).
4. Crush the bacon and add to the salad. Pour the dressing over all and stir well until the salad is well coated. Divide between 2 plates and serve.

Toasted Ham, Swiss, And Arugula Sandwiches

This toasted sandwich omits the fat of the typical grilled ham and cheese and adds a lot more crunch. Served with a light soup or a salad, this is a delicious and healthy lunchtime meal.

Ingredients

- 8 slices reduced-calorie whole wheat bread
- 2 teaspoons Dijon mustard
- 2 pound (about 2 6 slices) thinly sliced lean deli ham
- 8 slices reduced-fat Swiss cheese
- 2 cup fresh arugula

Preparations

1. Preheat the oven to 4 65 degrees F.
2. Separate four slices of the bread with the Dijon mustard, and top with about 4 slices of ham and 2 Slices of cheese.

3. Top each with 1/2 cup arugula and place the remaining bread slices onto the sandwiches. Bake in the oven center for 6 minutes, turn over, and then bake until the cheese is melted and the bread is golden. Divide each sandwich in half and serve hot.

Power-Packed Green Smoothie

Even if you don't have time for Much of a lunch, you'll still have time to get a heaping helping of minerals and vitamins in the form of this smoothie. The healthy fat from the avocado and the fiber from the vegetables Mean you'll feel satisfied, too.

Ingredients

- 2 medium cucumber, peeled and chopped
- 2 Cups fresh baby spinach
- 1 cup fresh parsley
- 2 cup carrot juice
- 1 teaspoon salt
- 2 dashes red pepper hot sauce
- 1 avocado, chopped

Preparations

1. Combine the cucumber, spinach, parsley, carrot juice, salt, and hot sauce in a blender and blend on high until smooth.

2. Add the avocado and blend on medium speed until smooth. Divide between 4 glasses and serve immediately.

Quick And Light White Bean Chili

This chili takes no time (and only one pan) to cook, and it tastes even better the next day. It also freezes well, so ensure to make a double batch to portion and store in the freezer for busy days.

Ingredients

- 2 teaspoon olive oil
- 2 pound freshly ground turkey breast
- 2 teaspoon chili powder
- 2 teaspoon salt
- 1 tsn freshly ground black pepper
- 1 teaspoon ground cumin
- 2 cup diced white fresh onion
- 2 tablespoons chopped fresh cilantro
- 2 (2 6 -ounce) cans great northern beans, undrained
- 2 Cups chicken stock

Preparations

1. Heat the olive oil in a saucepan. Add the turkey, chili powder, salt, pepper, and cumin and sauté and saute for 8 to 8 minutes, chopping often with the spatula, until the turkey is cooked through.

2. Add the fresh onion and sauté for 2 minute more before adding the cilantro, beans with liquid, and chicken stock. Bring to a boil, and minimize the heat to low, cover, and let simmer for 2 10 minutes. Divide between 4 soup bowls and serve hot.

Eggplant, Hummus, And Goat Cheese Sandwiches

Grilled slices of eggplant replace deli meats, and hummus adds protein and fiber while taking the place of mayonnaise. Try this classic Greek recipe and bring a Mediterranean flair to your lunch table.

Ingredients

- 2 medium eggplant, sliced 1 inch thick
- Sea salt
- 2 tablespoons olive oil
- Freshly ground black pepper
- 6 to 6 tablespoons hummus
- 4 slices whole wheat bread, toasted
- 2 cup baby spinach leaves
- 2 ounces goat cheese or feta cheese, softened

Preparations

1. Preheat a gas or charcoal grill to medium-high heat.

2. Add salt to each sides of the eggplant that has been sliced, and let it sit for few minutes to drain out the bitter juices. Rinse the eggplant and dry with a paper towel.

3. Brush the eggplant with the olive oil then season to taste with salt and pepper.

4. Grill the eggplant until lightly charred on both sides but still slightly firm in the middle, 4 to 4 minutes per side.

5. Spread the hummus on 2 Slices of the bread and top with the spinach leaves, goat cheese, and eggplant. Top with the rest of the slices of bread and serve warm.

Vegetable Market Scramble

There's nothing wrong with breakfast for lunch. This dish cooks up in just a few Minutes and will keep you going all day long.

Ingredients

- 2 teaspoon olive oil
- 1 red bell pepper, diced
- 1 cup diced white fresh onion
- 2 cup sliced fresh mushrooms
- 1 teaspoon salt
- 1/2 teaspoon freshly ground black pepper
- 8 fresh eggs, beaten

Preparations

1. Heat the olive oil in a skillet. Add the bell pepper, fresh onion , mushrooms, salt, and pepper and sauté for 6   minutes, stirring frequently.

2. Pour the eggs over all and scramble, stirring constantly, for about 4 minutes, or until the eggs are set. Divide between 4 plates and serve hot.

Tangy Orange Chicken Breast

This recipe delivers on both speed and flavor. It's a terrific dish to whip up on busy nights. Served with a green salad and some quinoa or brown rice, it's a light but satisfying Meal.

Ingredients

- 2 teaspoon olive oil
- 4 (4-to 6 -ounce) skinless chicken breasts
- 2 teaspoon paprika
- 1 teaspoon salt
- 1/2 teaspoon freshly ground black pepper
- 2 teaspoon chopped fresh thyme
- 2 teaspoon chopped fresh rosemary
- 2 tablespoon unsweetened orange juice concentrate
- 2 tablespoons chopped fresh parsley

Preparations

1. Preheat the oven to 400° F and line a baking dish with aluminum foil. Spread the olive oil all over the bottom of the dish.
2. Place the chicken breasts in the dish, flip over to coat with oil, and season with the paprika, salt, pepper, thyme, and rosemary.
3. Bake for 25 minutes, and flip the chicken and brush with the orange juice concentrate. Bake for 2 6 to 25 minutes more, or until the chicken juices run clear.
4. Garnish with the parsley before serving.

Grilled Shrimp And Black Bean Salad

This recipe is the best one to use when you have company for dinner. No one will think it's low-calorie!

Ingredients

- 2 teaspoon lime zest (about 1 lime)
- 1/2 cup freshly squeezed lime juice
- 4 tablespoons olive oil
- 2 tablespoons chopped fresh basil
- 2 tablespoons chopped fresh oregano
- 2 teaspoon freshly ground black pepper
- 1 teaspoon salt
- 2 cans black beans, washed and drained
- 2 cup diced tomatoes
- 2 cup diced green bell pepper

- 1 cup chopped green fresh onion s
- 24 fresh (22 –30 Count) raw shrimp, peeled and deveined

Preparation

1. In a medium bowl, combine the juice and lime zest, olive oil, basil, oregano, and pepper and mix well. Measure 2 tablespoons out into a small bowl and set aside.

2. Add the salt, black beans, tomatoes, bell pepper, and fresh onion s to the medium bowl and toss well. Place in the refrigerator until serving.

3. Preheat a flat grill over medium-high heat. Once hot, place the shrimp on the grill and baste with the reserved lime juice mixture. Cook for about five mins on one side and then turn, baste

again, and cook for 4 minutes more.

4. To serve, place one-quarter of the bean salad onto each plate and top with 6 hot shrimp.

Mustard-Maple-Glazed Salmon

This is an incredibly delicious recipe for salmon, especially given how quick and simple it is to prepare. Add some brown rice or a baked sweet potato and you have a flavorful, rich Meal.

Ingredients

- 4 (6-ounce) skin-on salmon fillets, ¾ inch thick
- 2 teaspoon olive oil
- 1 teaspoon salt
- 1 teaspoon freshly ground black pepper
- 2 tablespoons pure maple syrup
- 1 teaspoon dry mustard
- 8 sprigs fresh thyme

Preparation

1. Preheat a flat grill over medium-high heat.
2. Brush the salmon fillets on each sides with the olive oil, season with pepper and salt, and put them all skin side down on the grill. Cook for 8 minutes.
3. Meanwhile, combine the maple syrup and dry mustard with a fork.
4. Flip the salmon fillets, brush with the maple-mustard glaze, and top each one with 2 Sprigs of the thyme. Grill for 6 to 2 o minutes more, or until the fish flakes easily.
5. To serve, make use of a spatula to transfer the fillets to 4 plates, leaving the thyme intact.

Tuscan-Style Baked Sea Bass

Sea bass is a tasty fish—fine and flaky. This Tuscan-inspired recipe complements this Mild fish with the flavors of fresh tomatoes, walnuts, basil, and garlic

Ingredients

- 4 (6-ounce) skin-on sea bass fillets
- 2 teaspoon olive oil
- 2 cup very finely chopped walnuts (use processor or blender)
- 2 teaspoons minced garlic
- 8 slices yellow or orange tomatoes, 1/2 inch thick
- 8 slices red fresh onion , 1/2 inch thick
- 1 cup chopped fresh basil
- 1 teaspoon salt
- 1/2 teaspoon freshly ground black pepper

148

Preparation

1. Preheat the oven to 400ºF and line a baking sheet with aluminum foil.

2. Brush both sides of the bass fillets with the olive oil and then dip in the chopped walnuts, covering the fillets fully. Put the fillets skin all side down on the baking sheet. Spread the garlic over the fillets, then cover the fish with alternating tomato and fresh onion slices. Spray the basil on top and season with pepper and salt.

3. Bake for 2 2 to 2 4 minutes, or until the fish flakes easily. To serve, make use of a spatula to transfer the fillets to 4 plates.

Portobello Cheeseburgers

It's not necessary you are a vegetarian to love these burgers, Made with succulent portobello mushrooms. They're deliciously different but every bit as satisfying as a traditional burger, without all the fat and calories. Cannellini beans tucked under the caps make them filling enough for even the hungriest eater.

Ingredients

- 4 fresh (4 inches wide) portobello mushroom caps
- 2 1 teaspoons olive oil, divided
- 1 teaspoon salt
- 1/2 teaspoon freshly ground black pepper
- 1 teaspoon minced garlic
- 1 teaspoon paprika
- 2 cup canned cannellini beans
- 4 (2 -ounce) slices reduced-fat mozzarella cheese
- 4 whole wheat hamburger buns

- 4 fresh leaves romaine lettuce
- 4 slices fresh tomato
- 8 slices red fresh onion

Preparation

1. Preheat the oven to 4 30 degrees F.
2. Rub the cap sides of the mushrooms with 1 teaspoon of the olive oil and season with salt and pepper.
3. In a skillet, heat the remaining 2 teaspoon olive oil over medium-high heat. Add the mushrooms, cap side down, and sauté for 4 minutes.
4. Meanwhile, mix together the garlic, paprika, and beans and heat in the microwave for 2 minute, or just until warm. Set aside.

5. Flip the mushrooms and place 2 slice of mozzarella onto each one. Reduce the heat to low.
6. Toast the hamburger buns in the oven for 6 minutes, or just until crisp. Transfer to 4 plates. Top the bottom buns with the tomato, lettuce, and fresh onion .
7. Spoon one-quarter of the bean mixture into a mound in the center of each bun and top with a mushroom, cap side up. Add the top buns and serve.

Flank Steak Spinach Salad

Flank steak is a flavorful and lean cut of Meat that is ideal for a low-calorie diet. This recipe calls for the steak to be cooked medium rare. The Meat tends to get quite tough if cooked much more than that.

Ingredients

- 2 pound flank steak, visible fat and sinew removed
- 1/2 cup Balsamic Vinaigrette, divided
- 1 teaspoon salt
- 1 teaspoon freshly ground black pepper
- 4 Cups chopped romaine lettuce
- 2 cup baby spinach leaves
- 2 pint cherry tomatoes, halved
- 1 cup thinly sliced sweet yellow fresh onion

Preparation

1. Preheat a flat grill over high heat until it is very hot.

153

2. Brush the flank steak with 2 tablespoons of the Balsamic Vinaigrette, season with the salt and pepper, and place on the grill. Cook for few minutes, flip and cook for 25 minutes more, or until the steak is medium rare.

3. Meanwhile, combine the lettuce, spinach, tomatoes, and fresh onion until well mixed. Then add the remaining 2 tablespoons vinaigrette dressing. Toss well to coat and divide the salad between 4 plates.

4. Transfer the flank steak to a plate and allow it to rest for 25 minutes before slicing thinly on the diagonal.

5. Place one-quarter of the sliced steak on top of each salad and serve.

Chicken Picadillo

This variation on a traditional Latin dish uses leaner chicken in place of beef. It takes nothing away from the zesty flavor, but it does reduce the fat and calories usually present in the traditional version. Make an extra ration to freeze for later.

Ingredients

- 2 teaspoons olive oil
- 1 cup chopped yellow fresh onion
- 2 Cloves garlic, chopped
- 1 pound ground chicken
- 1 teaspoon ground cumin
- 1 teaspoon salt
- 1/2 teaspoon freshly ground black pepper
- 2 tablespoons red wine
- 2 cup chopped tomato
- 2 fresh jalapeño pepper, seeded and diced
- 1/2 cup green olives with pimientos, chopped

- 2 teaspoon Worcestershire sauce
- 1/2 cup chopped fresh cilantro
- 2 teaspoon fresh lime juice (about 1 lime)

Preparation

1. Heat the olive oil in a skillet. Add the garlic and fresh onion then sauté for 2 minutes, stirring often.

2. Add the chicken, cumin, salt, and pepper and cook for 6 to 6 minutes, stirring frequently to crumble the chicken.

3. Add the wine into the pan to deglaze it, scraping any browned bits from the bottom. Add the tomato, jalapeño, olives, and Worcestershire sauce; reduce the heat to medium and let simmer for 8 minutes, or until the mixture has thickened.

4. To serve, ladle into 4 bowls and finish with a squeeze of lime and a sprinkling of cilantro.

Chicken Florentine-Style

In this riff on true Florentine dishes, chicken breasts are treated with a delicious creamy sauce studded with fresh spinach. Serve this one to your guests—they'll have no idea you're on a diet.

Ingredients

- 2 teaspoon olive oil
- 4 (6-ounce) boneless skinless chicken breasts
- 1 teaspoon salt
- 1/2 teaspoon freshly ground black pepper
- 1/2 cup dry white wine
- 1/2 cup chopped yellow fresh onion
- 2 cup sliced fresh mushrooms
- 2 cup ice-covered chopped spinach, defrosted and drained

- 1 cup chicken stock
- 1/2 cup low-fat milk
- 1/2 cup shredded Parmesan cheese

Preparation

1. Heat the olive oil in a skillet.
2. Season the chicken breasts on each sides with the salt and pepper and sauté for 10 minutes. Flip the chicken and cook for 6 to 8 minutes more, or until the juices run clear. Transfer to a plate then cover it to keep warm.
3. Add the wine to the pan to deglaze it, and scrape up any browned bits from the bottom.
4. Add the fresh onion , mushrooms, spinach, and chicken stock, and simmer for 25 to 2 6 minutes, or until the sauce is reduced by half.

5. Decrease the heat, stir in the milk, and heat just until warmed though, about 2 minute.
6. To serve, put one chicken breast on each plate, top with one-quarter of the sauce, and sprinkle with the Parmesan cheese.

Easy Black Bean Soup

When served with a fresh salad and a crusty roll, this dish is a comforting and filling Meal. You'll get all the flavors of traditional black bean soup but in far less time.

Ingredients

- 2 (2 6 -ounce) cans black beans
- 1 teaspoon chili powder
- 2 Cups chicken stock
- 2 cup thinly sliced carrots
- 1 cup chopped yellow fresh onion
- 1 teaspoon garlic powder
- 1 teaspoon ground cumin
- 1 teaspoon salt

- 1/2 teaspoon freshly ground black pepper
- 2 cup plain yogurt
- 1/2 cup sliced green fresh onion s

Preparation

1. Over medium heat, mix the black beans, chicken stock, carrots, fresh onion , garlic powder, cumin, chili powder, and salt in a saucepan. Stir well.
2. Boil the soup, reduce the heat to medium, cover, and simmer for 25 minutes, stirring occasionally.
3. To serve, ladle into 4 bowls, top with a fresh dollop of yogurt, and garnish with green fresh onion s.

Hearty Vegetable Soup

The vegetable soup is very easy to make and is just packed with a wide variety of vegetables. It's a great soup to serve alongside a salad or sandwich on those nights when you don't feel like cooking, so double up and freeze the extra.

Ingredients

- 2 teaspoon olive oil
- 2 cup diced Yukon Gold potatoes
- 1 cup thinly sliced carrots
- 1 cup fresh green beans, slice into 2 -inch pieces
- 1 cup chopped yellow fresh onion
- 2 cup fresh spinach leaves
- 4 Cups chicken stock
- 1/2 cup chopped fresh parsley
- 2   tablespoon chopped fresh rosemary
- 1 teaspoon salt
- 1/2 teaspoon freshly ground black pepper

Preparation

1. Heat the olive oil in a skillet. Add the potatoes, carrots, green beans, and fresh onion and sauté for 6 minutes, stirring frequently. Remove from the heat.

2. Transfer the vegetables to a fresh saucepan over medium-high heat. Add the spinach, chicken stock, parsley, rosemary, salt, and pepper and bring the soup to a boil. Reduce the heat, cover it, then simmer for 45 minutes.

3. To serve, ladle into 4 bowls.

Mushroom-Stuffed Zucchini

Fresh zucchini and mushrooms Seasoned with garlic, olive oil, parsley, and Italian herbs and spices hardly seems like diet food. These mushroom-stuffed zucchini boats Make an easy and impressive dish that is low in calories but still plenty filling. Serve with a piece of fish for dinner, or serve alone for lunch.

Ingredients

- 2 tablespoons olive oil
- 2 Cups finely chopped button mushrooms
- 2 Cloves garlic, finely chopped
- 2 tablespoons chicken stock
- 2 tablespoon finely chopped flat-leaf parsley
- 2 tablespoon Italian seasoning
- Sea salt
- Freshly ground black pepper

- 2 medium zucchini, cut in half lengthwise
- 2 tablespoon water

Preparation

1. Preheat the oven to 4 65 degrees F.
2. Heat a skillet, then add put in olive oil. Add the mushrooms, allow it to cook until tender, about 4 minutes. Add the garlic and cook for 2 minutes more. Add the chicken then cook for four minutes more.
3. Add the parsley and Italian seasoning, then season with salt and pepper to taste. Stir well and remove from the heat.
4. Scoop out some of the flesh and the seeds of the halved zucchini and stuff the halves with the mushroom mixture.

5. Put the zucchini inside a casserole dish, and drizzle 2 tablespoon water in the bottom.

6. Cover with aluminum foil and bake for 45 to 40 minutes, or until the zucchini boats are tender. Transfer to 2 plates and serve immediately.

Zesty Beef Kabobs

Tender, juicy, and zesty, these kabobs are going to Make you glad you're eating healthy. Yet more proof that eating lean doesn't have to taste unappetizing!

Ingredients

- 1 cup lime juice
- 2 teaspoon salt
- 2 teaspoon black pepper
- 2 clove garlic, minced
- 1/2 teaspoon red pepper flakes
- 1/2 teaspoon rosemary, chopped
- 1/2 teaspoon basil, chopped
- 2 pound lean red meat, such as beef, venison, or bison, chunked into bitesized cubes
- 2 red fresh onion , peeled, cut in half horizontally, and quartered vertically
- 2 pack cherry tomatoes
- 2 green peppers, cut similarly to the fresh onion

Preparation

1. Mix together the first seven ingredients.

2. Add meat to a fresh plastic zip bag, and pour the lime and spice mixture over it. Marinate for at least 25 minutes—the longer the better.

3. Preheat grill to medium/high when you're ready to make the kabobs. Thread the meat, fresh onion s, tomatoes, and peppers onto your skewers.

4. Grill 2 –4 minutes on each of the four sides, or until your steak reaches desired temp.

Pancakes With Cream Cheese

Ingredients:

60 g low-fat cream cheese

2 eggs

10 0 g almond flour

2 teaspoons agave syrup

2 25 ml almond milk

Coconut oil

Preparation:

Mix the cream cheese together with the eggs, almond flour, and agave syrup. Then add the almond milk little by little, stirring constantly, until the dough becomes thin.

Heat the coconut oil in the pan and add some batter to the pan. Swirl the pan so that

168

the batter spreads out and creates a pancake.

After a while, turn the pancake so that it browns evenly on both sides. Then place it on a kitchen towel to drain and repeat the process until the batter is used up.

Pomegranate Muesli

Ingredients:

45 g pomegranate seeds

230 g natural yogurt

1 teaspoon de-oiled raw cocoa powder

2 tbsp low-fat milk

45 g of oatmeal

4 almonds

Maple syrup or agave syrup

Preparation:

Lightly roast the oatmeal in the pan without oil and let it cool down afterwards.

Mix the yogurt with the milk and cocoa and add a little maple syrup.

Pour the chocolate yogurt into a bowl and add the coarsely chopped almonds and the roasted oat flakes. Carefully lift the pomegranate seeds out of the shell and add them as well. If you like cinnamon, you can sprinkle the whole thing with a little cinnamon.

Smoothie In The Bowl

Ingredients:

2 65 g yogurt

25 g raspberries

25 g blueberries

1/2 bananas

1/2 apples

25 g roasted oatmeal

2 teaspoon poppy seeds

2 teaspoon pumpkin seeds

4 almonds

Agave syrup

Preparation:

Wash and drain the fruit. Then put them in a blender jar along with the banana and apple. Also put the yogurt in the blender jar and puree everything finely. If necessary, sweeten it with agave syrup and then pour it into a bowl.

Finally, add the poppy seeds, roasted oat flakes, nuts and seeds to the yogurt mixture. You can add chia seeds, raisins and other nuts if you like.

Cinnamon Applesauce

Ingredients:
4 00g apples
1 teaspoon fresh Lemon juice
230 ml of water
Agave syrup
Cinnamon

Preparation:

Quarter the apples and remove the core. Then cut them into pieces and put them in a saucepan with water and fresh Lemon juice. Cook the whole thing with cinnamon for about 6 to 25 minutes until the apples are soft.

Then turn the soft apple pieces. If you would like it a little more liquid, you can add the pieces to the liquor with a ladle. Otherwise, you should use a ladle.

Sweeten the applesauce with a little agave syrup and refine it again with cinnamon afterwards. Let the applesauce cool.

Coconut Chia Pudding

Ingredients:

2 tbsp coconut flakes

Agave syrup

Cinnamon

230 ml almond milk

25 g chia seeds

45g blueberries

Preparation:

Mix the almond milk with the chia seeds and let them soak for at least 2 10 minutes.

Then add the washed blueberries and coconut flakes to the mixture and season with cinnamon and agave syrup.

Low Carb Chips

Ingredients:
4 00g zucchini
Paprika powder
2 tbsp olive oil
Salt pepper

Preparation:
Wash and dry the zucchini. Then cut off the ends and slice them into wafer-thin slices.

Place the slices on a parchment-lined baking sheet so they're not stacked on top of each other. Salt the slices and let them steep for about 10 minutes.

Then pour the olive oil over the slices and season them with paprika powder and pepper.

Then bake them in the oven at 230   degrees
for 2 2 minutes until they are golden brown.

Mug Cake From The Microwave

Ingredients:

2 egg

4 tbsp low-fat milk

2 1 tbsp almond flour

1 teaspoon baking powder

2 tbsp agave syrup

Salt

Preparation:

Mix the almond flour with the baking powder, a pinch of salt and the agave syrup in a cup.

Mix the egg with the low-fat milk separately and then add it to the flour mixture.

Then place the mug in the microwave on full power for 4 minutes.

This is a basic mug cake recipe. You can add blueberries or dark chocolate to the cake, for example.

Quark Buns

Ingredients

2 00g quinoa
85 g low-fat quark
85 g Greek yogurt

2 eggs

1 packet of baking powder

1 tbsp almond flour

4 tbsp psyllium husk

Salt

Preparation:

Wash and cook the quinoa until it is firm to the bite. At the same time, preheat the oven to approx. 230　degrees and line a baking sheet with baking paper.

Mix all ingredients together until dough is formed and form small rolls out of the dough. If the dough is too moist, you should add more almond flour. Should he be too dry?

Bake the buns at 230　degrees for about 45 minutes until they are golden brown. Avoid opening the oven while it is baking. This prevents the buns from collapsing.

Conclusion

I sincerely hope you are now equipped with a solid understanding of exactly what intermittent fasting is. Just as importantly, it is my wish that you are aware of the safe way for a woman to go about getting started with this lifestyle. There are a wide variety of methods that you can utilize on your fasting journey, the end goal is that all of them lead to the same destination: a healthier and happier you!

Remember that you are in control of your nutrition, health, and overall wellness. You do not have to follow intermittent fasting to achieve your goals, but this lifestyle is certainly a valuable tool to assist you with the health and physique you are striving for. Always remember that you are the one in control of what you eat and when you eat. If you choose to use intermittent fasting, that is a conscious choice that you are in complete control over. Never let any diet or exercise regimen gain control of you.

Intermittent fasting, although not a new idea by any means, has reemerged into the spotlight of the health and fitness industry and is now becoming the go-to nutrition plan for many people. If you sincerely commit to taking action and you try out this lifestyle for yourself, then it might just be the exact tool you needed to reach the health and weight goals that you desire. Now you have gained the understanding of how the female body works with intermittent fasting, and the knowledge of what to do, the choice is yours!

CPSIA information can be obtained
at www.ICGtesting.com
Printed in the USA
BVHW041736301020
592228BV00014B/131